Colour Me
DOG

First Published in the UK in 2016 by
Apple Press
74-77 White Lion Street
London N1 9PF
UK
www.apple-press.com

10 9 8 7 6 5 4 3 2

Manufactured in China

ISBN: 978-1-8454-3658-2

Publisher: Mark Searle
Editorial Director: Isheeta Mustafi
Commissioning Editor: Alison Morris
Junior Editor: Abbie Sharman
Editor: Joanne Reeder
Cover design: Michelle Rowlandson
Layout: Michelle Rowlandson and Agata Rybicka

TRIANIMALS

Colour Me DOG

60 Colour-by-Number
Geometric Artworks with Bark

ÇETIN CAN KARADUMAN

APPLEPRESS

Welcome to
TRIANIMALS

Spanish Water Dog
18

Weimaraner
19

Bullmastiff
20

Bichon Frise
21

Hungarian Vizsla
22

Komondor
23

Rhodesian Ridgeback
24

Greyhound
25

Bull Terrier
26

Irish Wolfhound
28

Poodle
29

Rough Collie
30

Border Terrier
31

Cocker Spaniel
32

Rottweiler
33

Saluki
34

Golden Retriever
35

German Shepherd
36

Afghan Hound
38

Great Dane
39

Beagle
40

English Springer Spaniel
41

Old English Sheepdog
42

Husky
43

Pekingese
44

Bernese Mountain Dog
45

Chinese Crested
46

Lhasa Apso
48

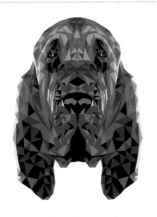

Bloodhound
49

Pug
50

Jack Russell Terrier
51

Shar Pei
52

Maltese
53

Australian Silky Terrier
54

Cockapoo
55

Airedale Terrier
56

Bouvier des Flandres

58

French Bulldog

59

Whippet

60

Papillon

61

Pomeranian

62

Pembroke Welsh Corgi

63

Fox Terrier

64

Australian Kelpie

65

Dachshund

66

Staffordshire Bull Terrier

68

Dalmatian

69

Doberman Pinscher

70

Akita
71

German Wirehaired Pointer
72

Boxer
74

Shih Tzu
75

MASKS

Chihuahua
81

Labrador
83

English Bulldog
85

St. Bernard
87

Border Collie
89

Chow Chow
91

Miniature Schnauzer
93

Basset Hound
95

HERE COME THE DOGS!

Welcome to the wonderful world of Trianimals. In this book you will find a pack of dogs that have been illustrated using hundreds of triangles of varying sizes. Whether it's a Pug, Beagle, Husky, Greyhound or French Bulldog, it's time to choose your favourite canine and get colouring.

The colours used in the palettes are as close to the real thing as possible, meaning that four-legged friends come to life on every page. Each hound in the book has very different facial features, attitudes, patterns, colour combinations and characteristics – carefully colour in the images and watch as the dogs start to reveal themselves, leaping out of the pages in glorious technicolour.

Colouring is the perfect pastime, aiding relaxation and allowing you to focus all your energy on a calm, quiet activity. So lose yourself in the pages of this book and discover talents you never knew you had. You can also join us online! Share your coloured-in animal on social media using the hashtag #Trianimals.

FROM THE AUTHOR

When thinking about creating this book, I found inspiration in many areas: walking around my local park, photographs online and also computer graphics. I wanted to experiment, test my capabilities, and this book is the result. Why triangles? It's the shape that offers the most variety, they work very well together and enable me to create complex images of each dog by using different sizes and combinations.

I have always loved dogs so was naturally drawn to using them as my subject matter. They are all so different, with unique characteristics, colours and personalities. I hope you enjoy colouring them as much as I enjoyed creating them.

MATERIALS

Invest in a pack of coloured pencils or felt-tip pens, and try to replicate the lightness and darkness of each shade. It's the light and dark triangles sitting side by side that give the images their depth and amazing 3-D look.

If you don't have coloured pencils or felt-tip pens, you could try watercolours or paint, and mix your own colours to create the right shade. But stay away from pastels as these are quite thick and it will be difficult to fill in the smaller triangles. Avoid charcoal too as this is likely to smudge, ruining all your hard work.

TECHNIQUES

Stay inside the lines and keep your pencils sharp so you have maximum control in the smaller areas. Sharpen your pencils frequently to achieve crisp, clean images.

If the colour of your pencil doesn't quite match our colour palette, try blending, cross-hatching and adding more layers until you get the colour you want. Take your time – a masterpiece was never created in a day!

If you are struggling to create a particular shade, try substituting that colour for one you have available, or you could create your own colour palette – just remember to keep dark shades dark and light shades light.

To achieve a darker shade, try layering the colour until you get the right shade. Pressing harder with your coloured pencil should also achieve this result.

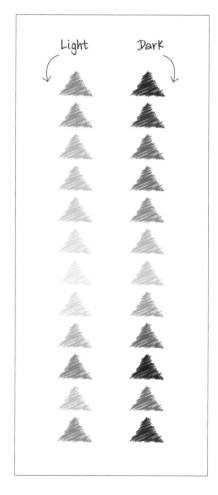

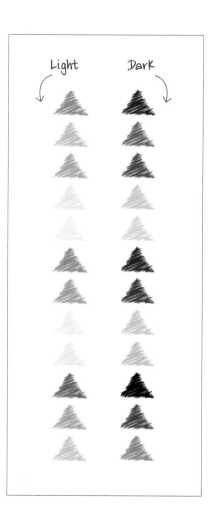

USING THE COLOUR PALETTE

Two colour palettes have been created alongside the illustrations in this book. The natural palette is based on the dog's natural colouring and the vivid palette can be used to create a more vibrant and graphic look.

NO NUMBER?
On the main illustration, if a triangle doesn't have a number that area is white, so there is no need to colour it in.

USING THE NATURAL PALETTE
The key to getting your dogs to look like the original image is to follow the natural palette as closely as possible.

USING THE VIVID PALETTE
If you're looking for something a bit brighter, or just a bit different, try our vivid colour palettes.

FREESTYLING
Avid colourers will spot that there are no colour palettes on the patterned pages for the Chinese crested, bull terrier or Airedale terrier. There are also 'colour me in' versions of the openers for each section. These dogs have been left unnumbered so you can let your imagination run wild. This is your chance to experiment with different colours and techniques. Why not create your own colour palette around your favourite colour, or create a wacky pattern using a pop art style?

For the best results, think about your shading. Imagine where the sun would catch the dog in real life and try to keep those areas lighter than areas in the shade. The diagrams on page 12 show how the same colour can be used in different ways to achieve this.

Look out for the animal's natural colour palette at the top of each design.

Saluki

Are you ready to experiment? Try the vivid colour palette at the bottom of the page.

Spanish Water Dog

1 2 3 4 5 6 7

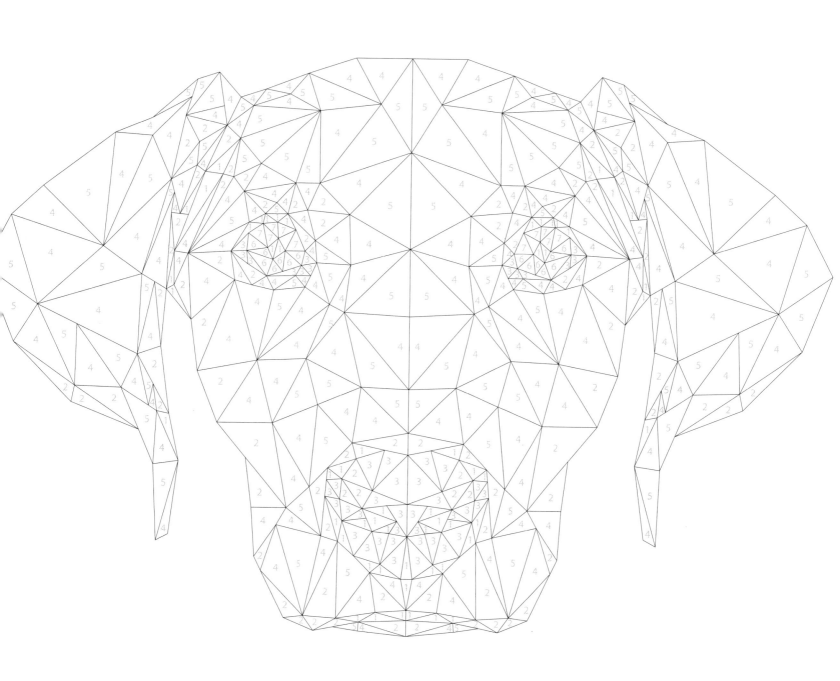

1 2 3 4 5 6 7

Bullmastiff

Bichon Frise

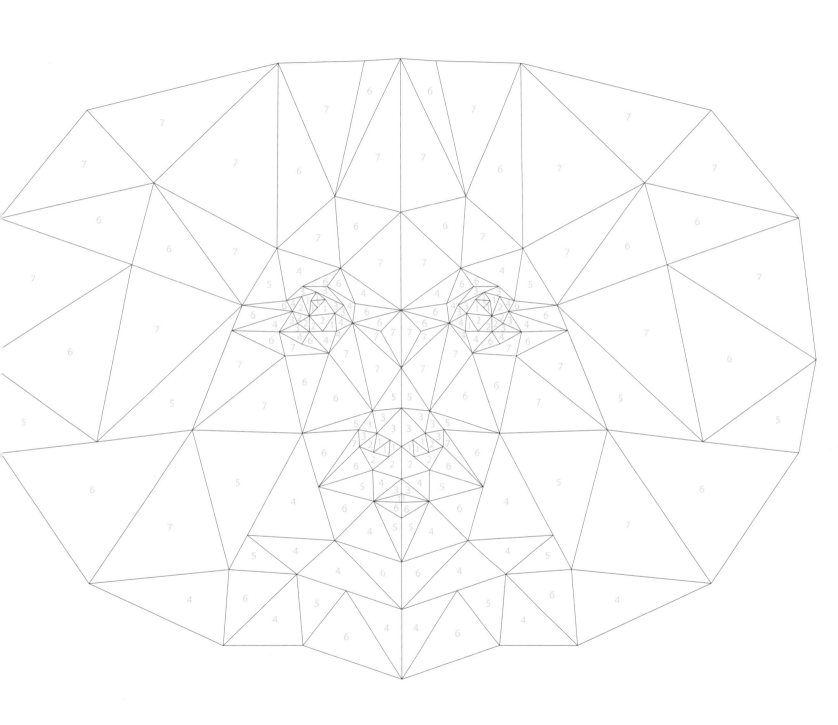

Hungarian Vizsla

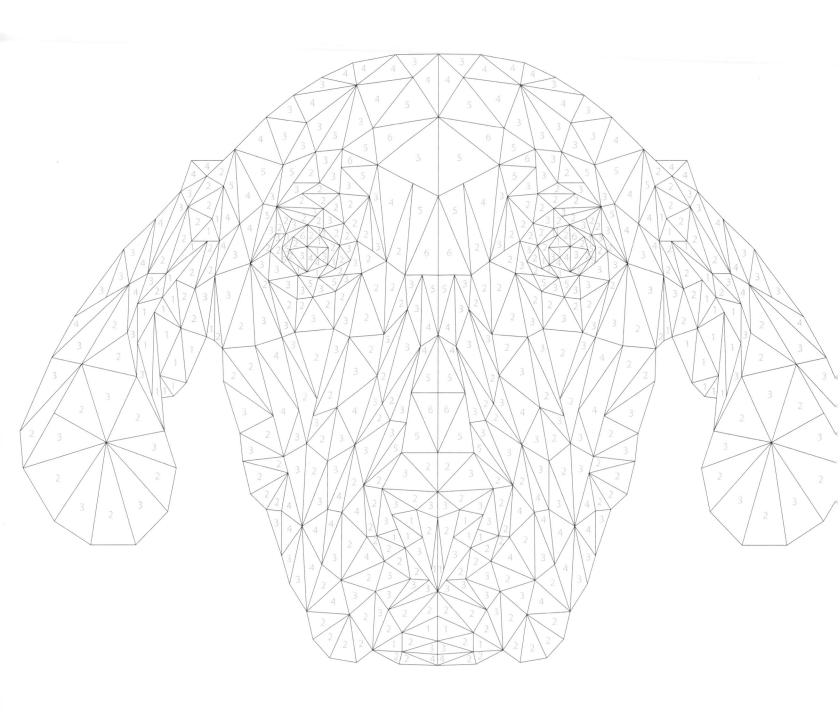

VIVID

Rhodesian Ridgeback

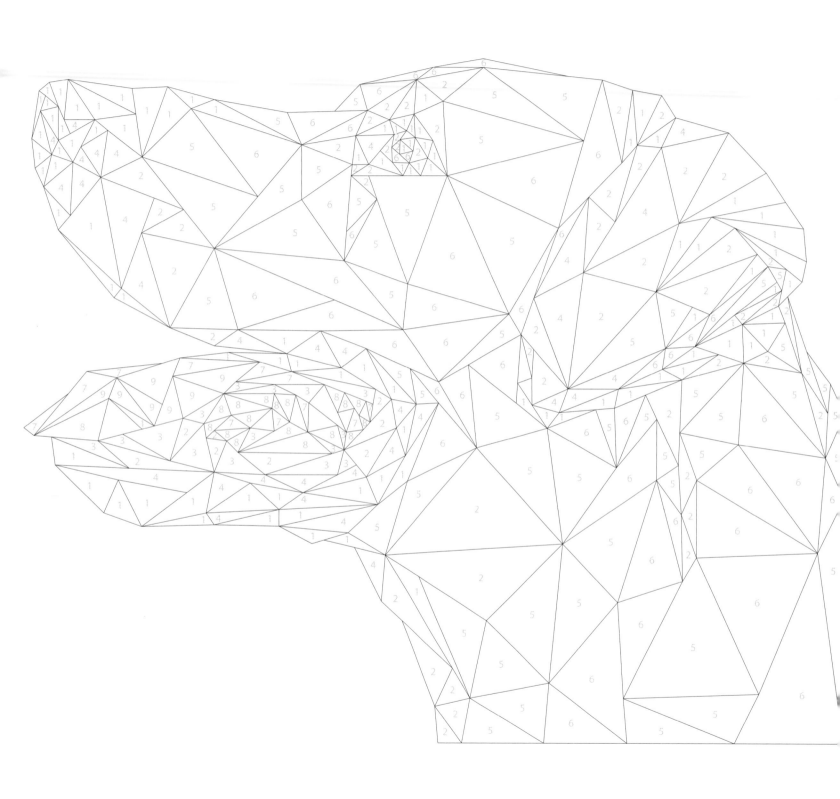

Greyhound

Bull Terrier

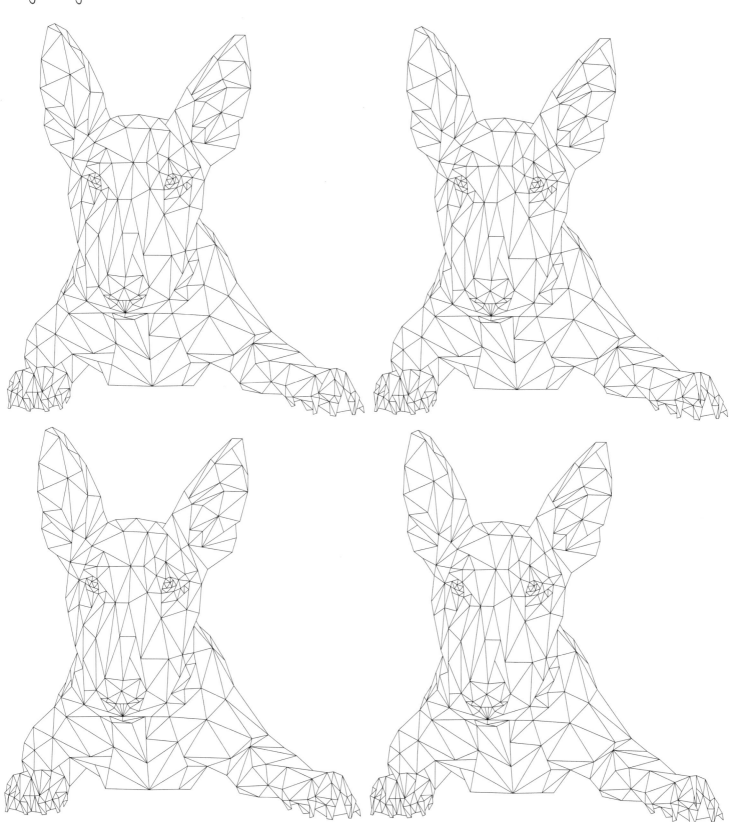

Irish Wolfhound

1   2   3   4   5   6

Poodle

1   2   3   4   5   6

Rough Collie

1 2 3 4 5 6 7

Cocker Spaniel

Rottweiler

Saluki

Golden Retriever

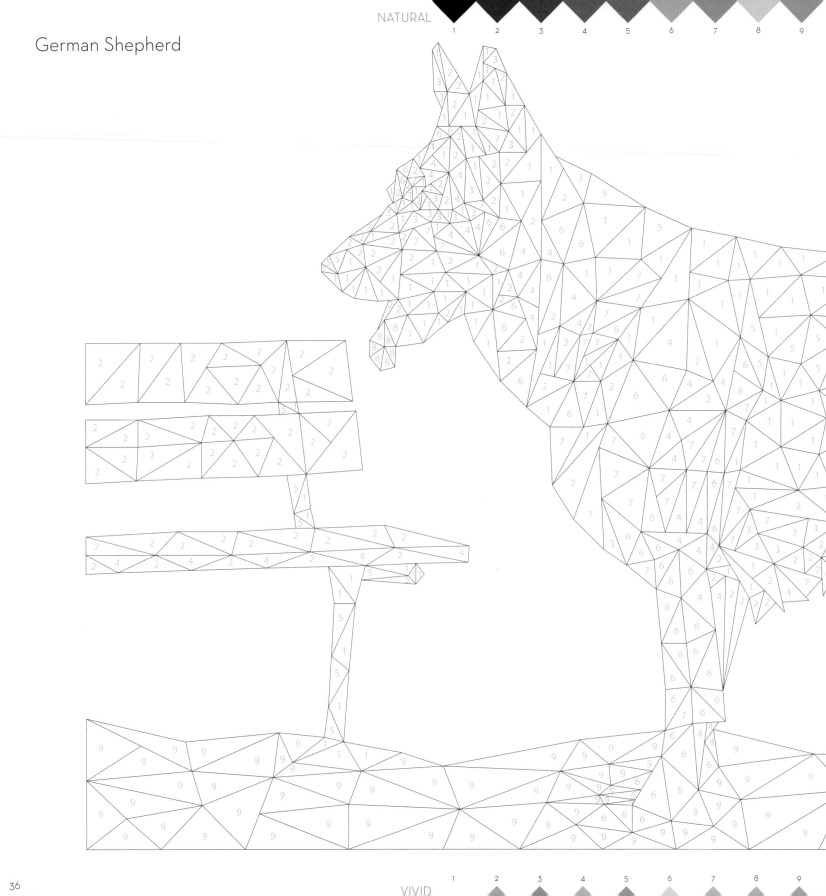

German Shepherd

NATURAL

VIVID

36

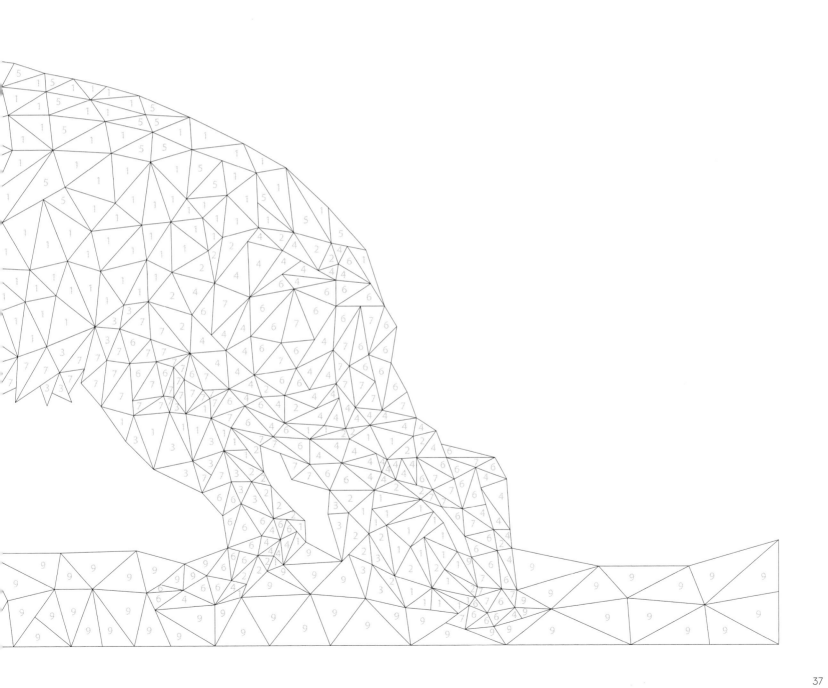

Afghan Hound

NATURAL

1 2 3 4 5 6 7 8 9

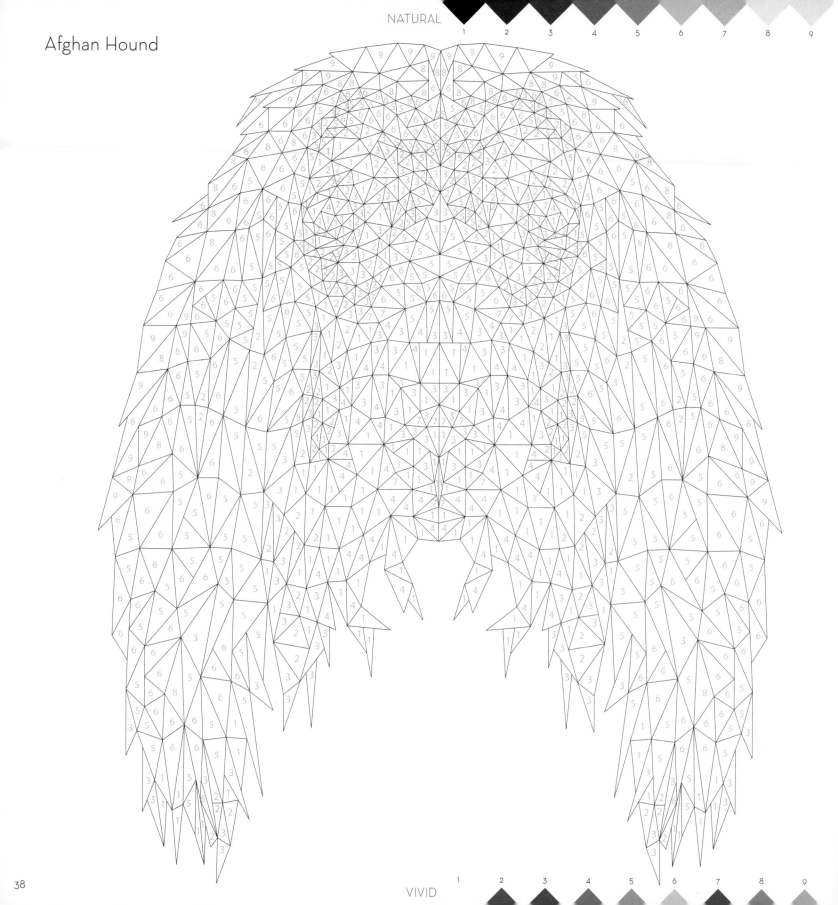

38

1 2 3 4 5 6 7 8 9

VIVID

Beagle

English Springer Spaniel

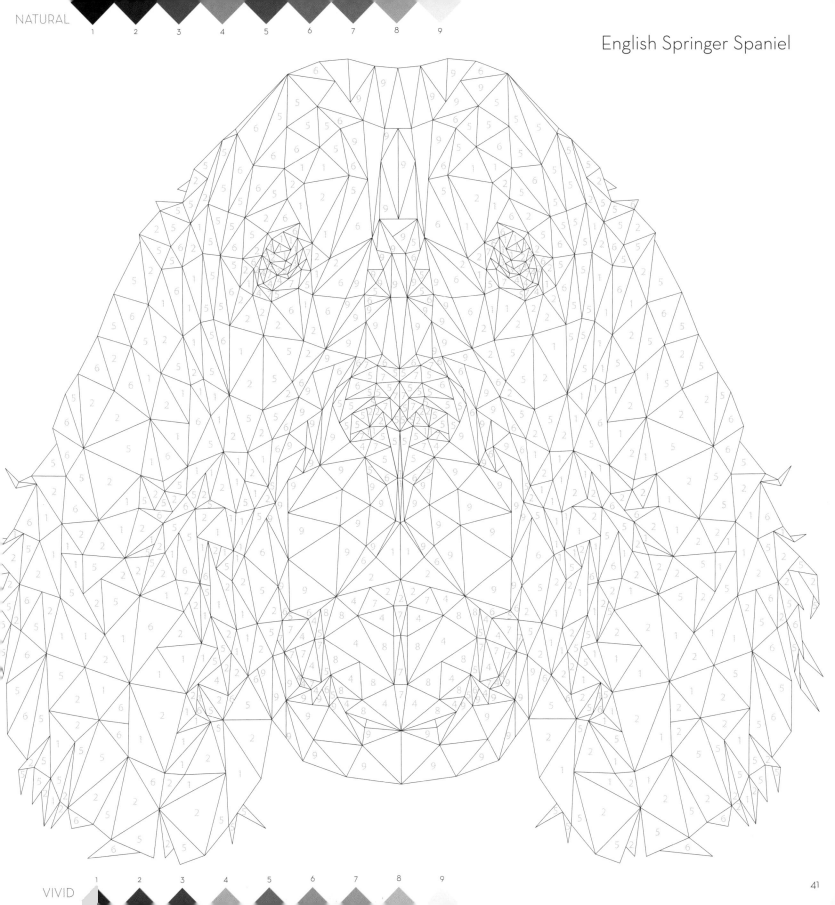

VIVID

Old English Sheepdog

1 2 3 4 5 6 7 8

Husky

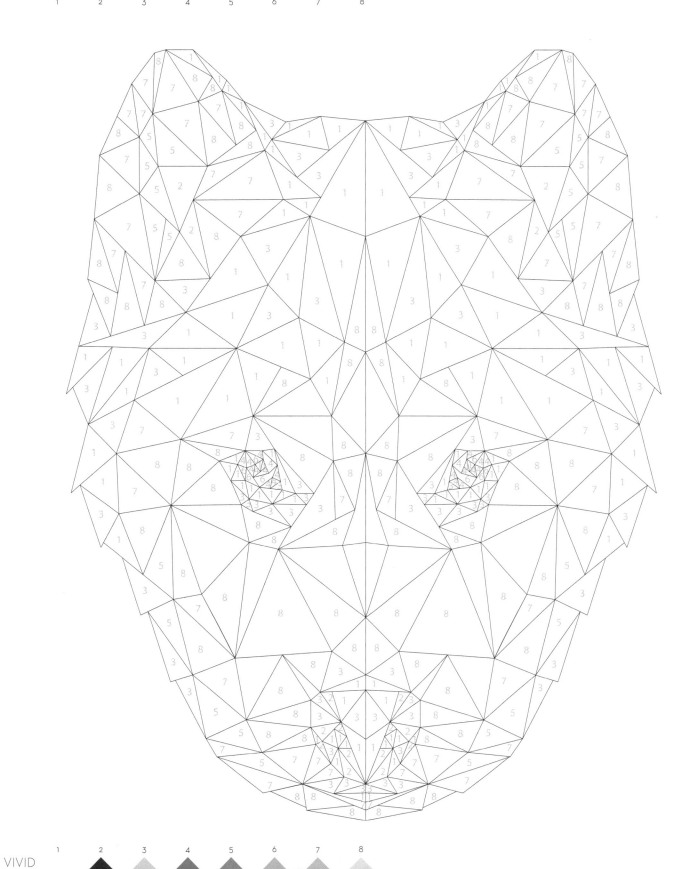

1 2 3 4 5 6 7 8

Pekingese

NATURAL 1 2 3 4 5 6 7

VIVID 1 2 3 4 5 6 7

Bernese Mountain Dog

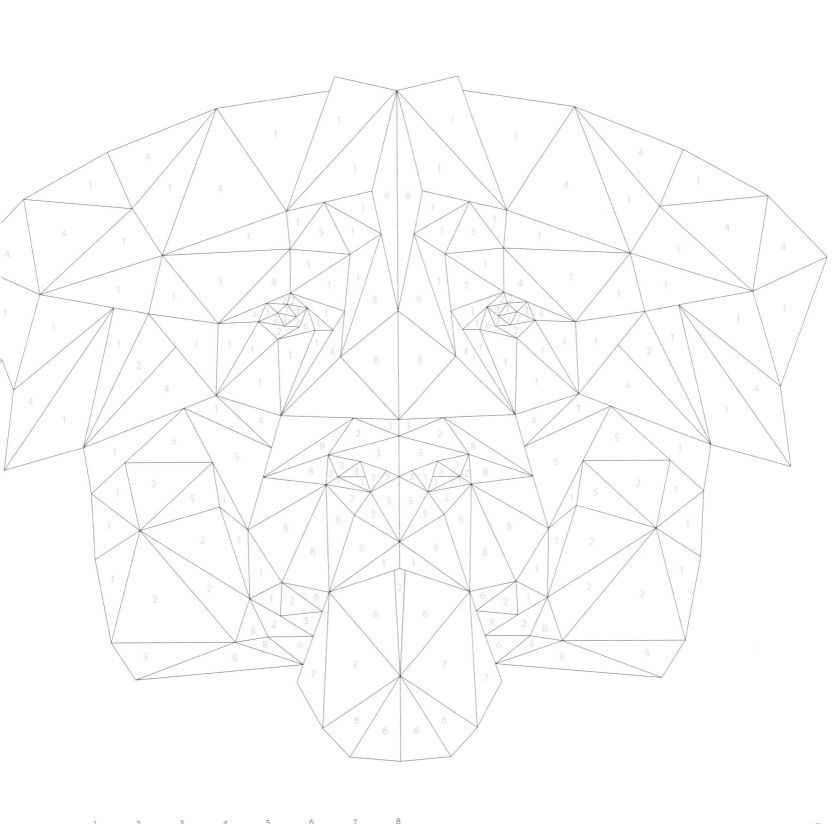

VIVID

Chinese Crested

VIVID

Freestyle with your own colours

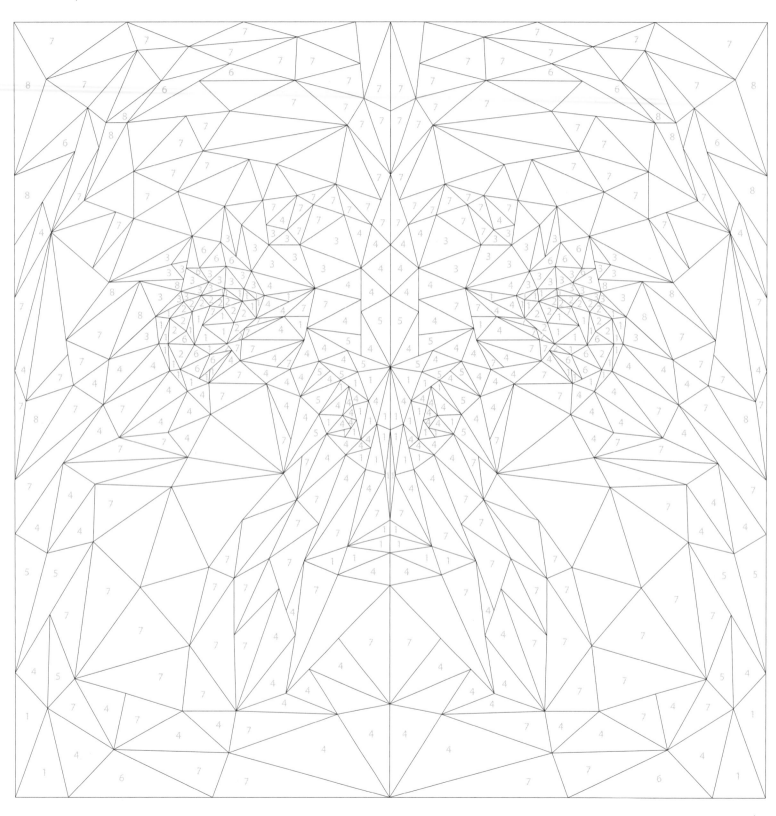

Lhasa Apso

VIVID

Bloodhound

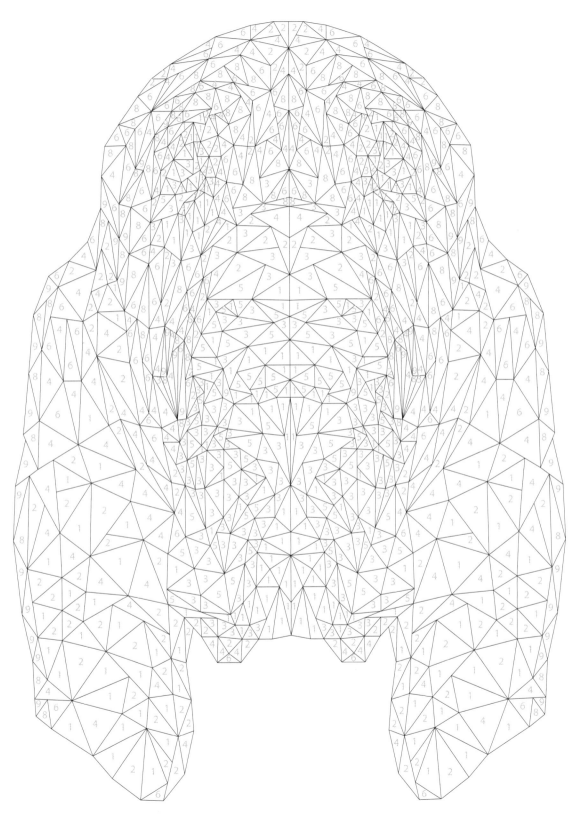

Pug

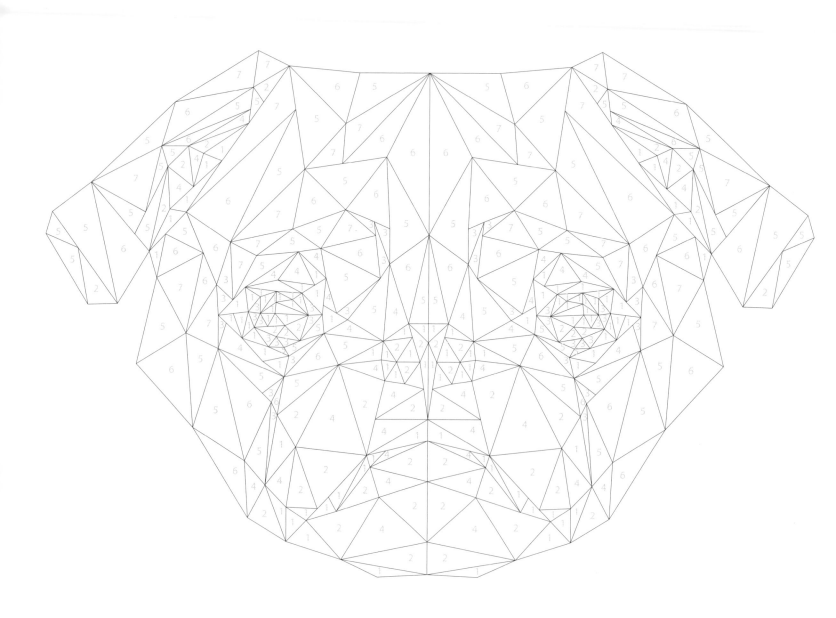

Jack Russell Terrier

Shar Pei

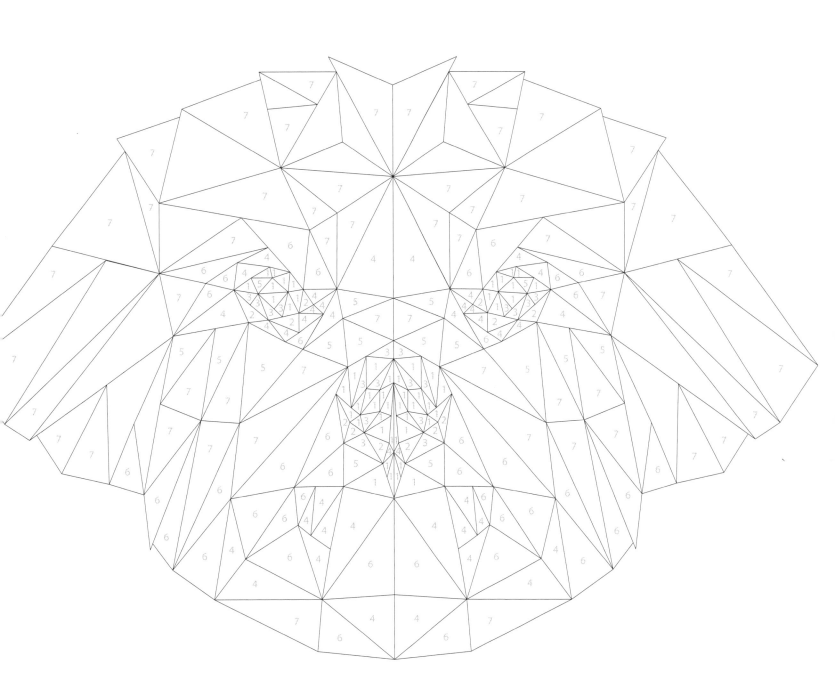

Australian Silky Terrier

Cockapoo

Airedale Terrier

VIVID

Freestyle with your own colours

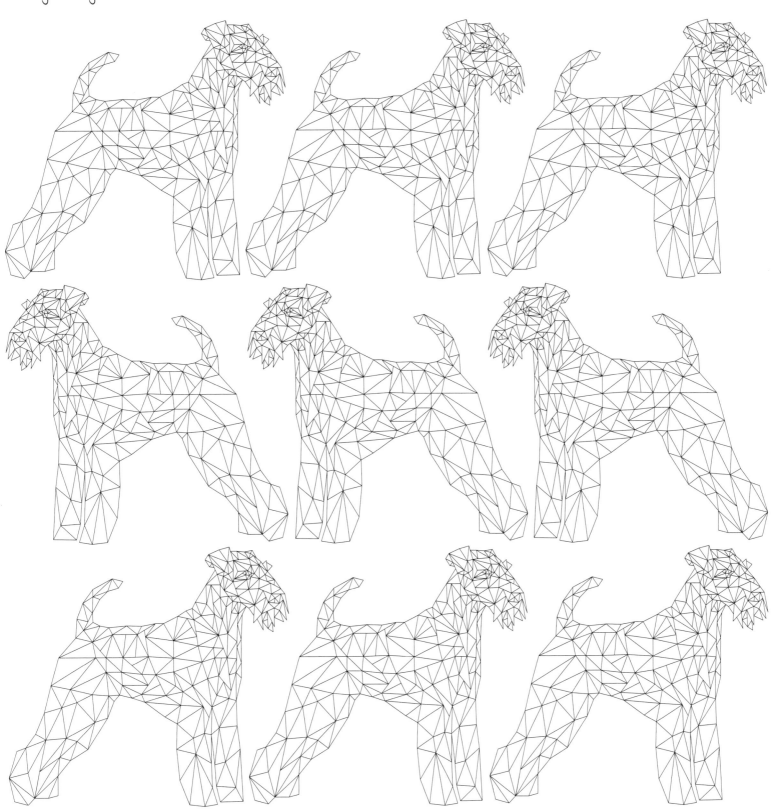

Bouvier des Flandres

French Bulldog

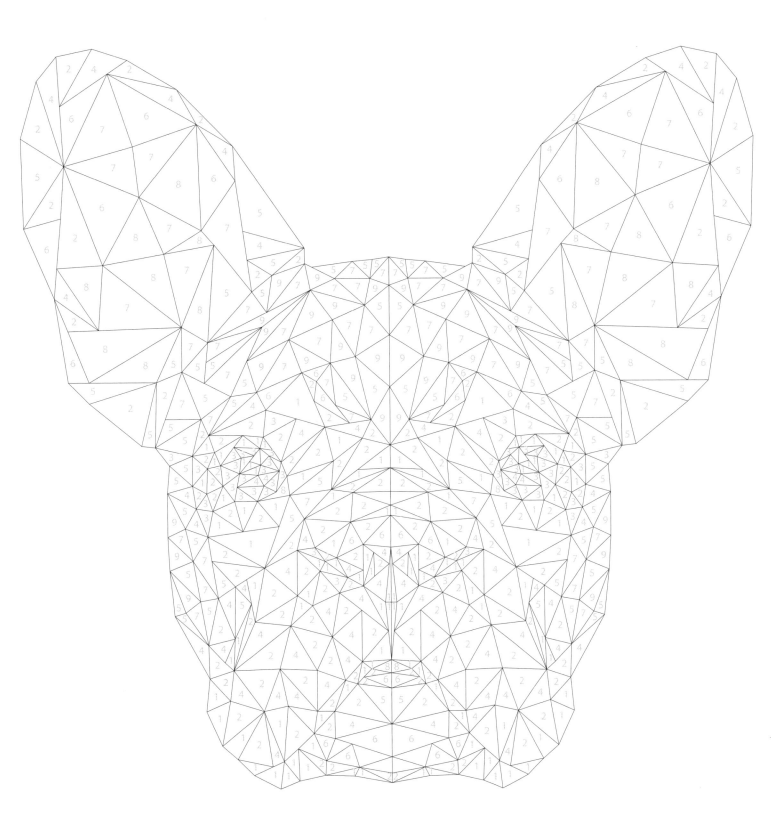

Whippet

Papillon

Pomeranian

1 2 3 4 5 6 7

Pembroke Welsh Corgi

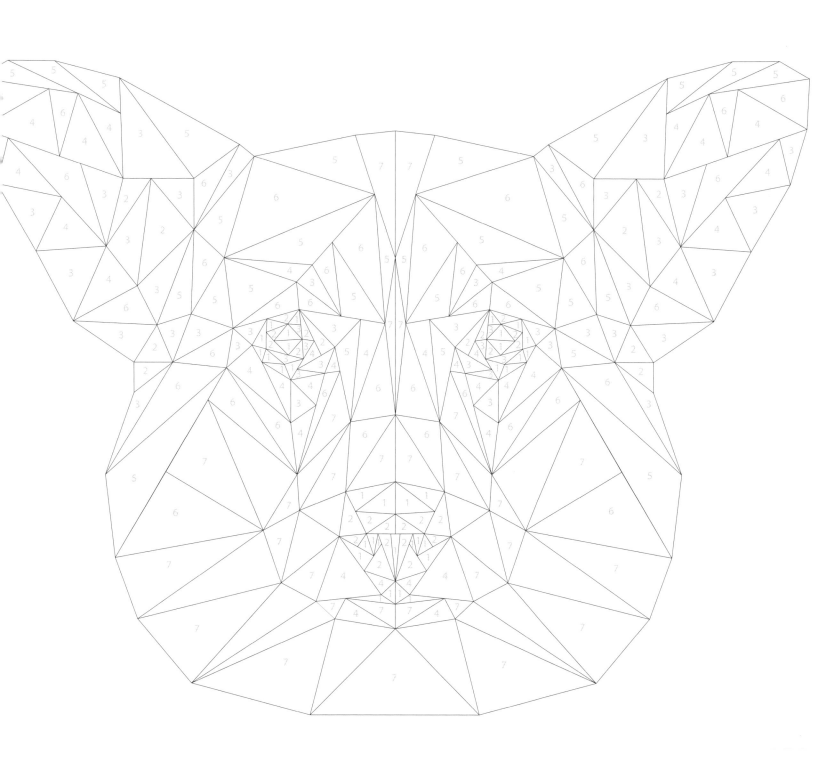

1 2 3 4 5 6 7

Fox Terrier

1 2 3 4 5 6 7

1 2 3 4 5 6 7

Dachshund

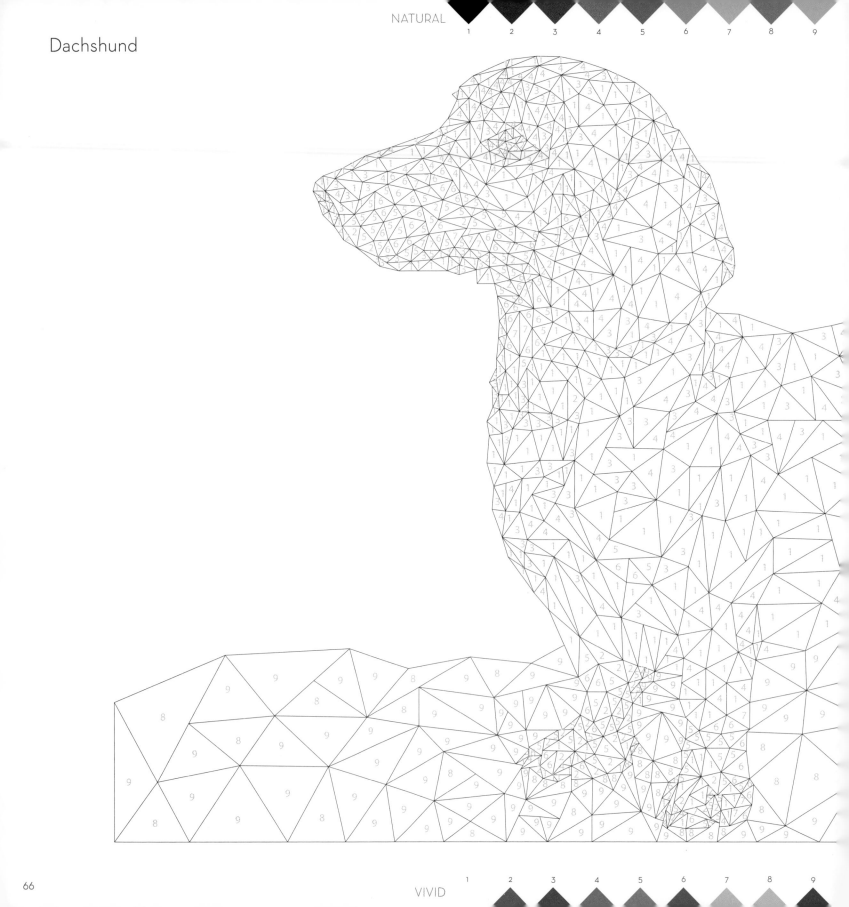

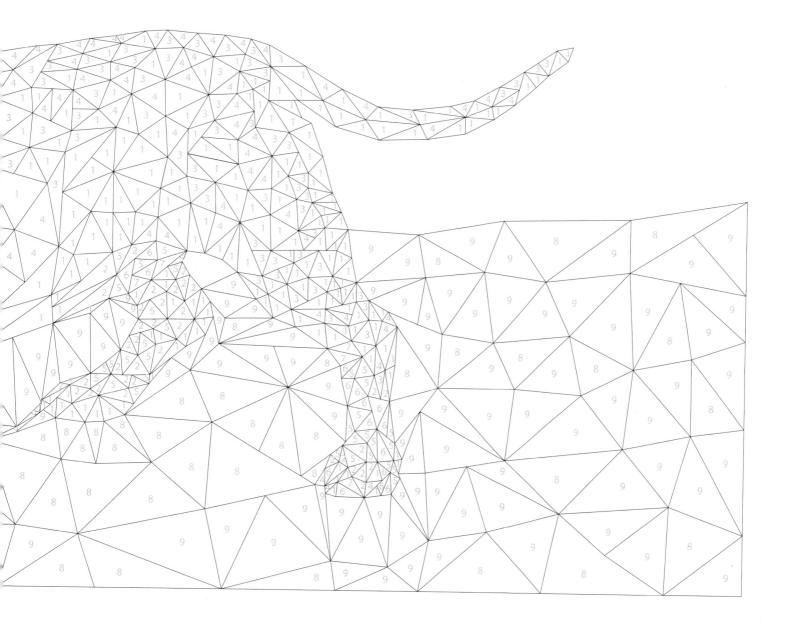

NATURAL

1 2 3 4 5 6 7 8

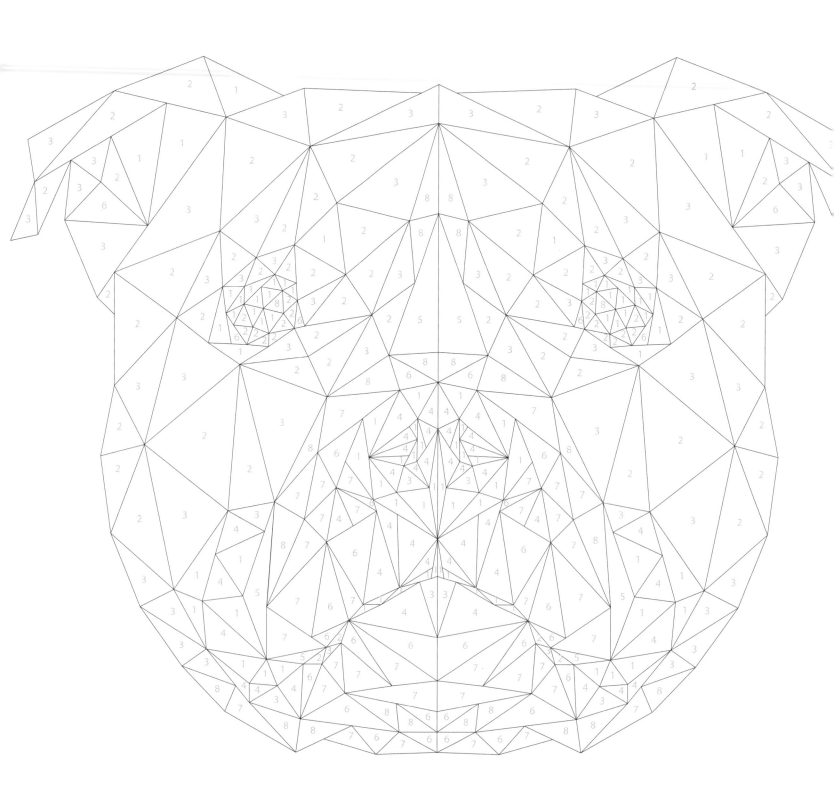

VIVID

1 2 3 4 5 6 7 8

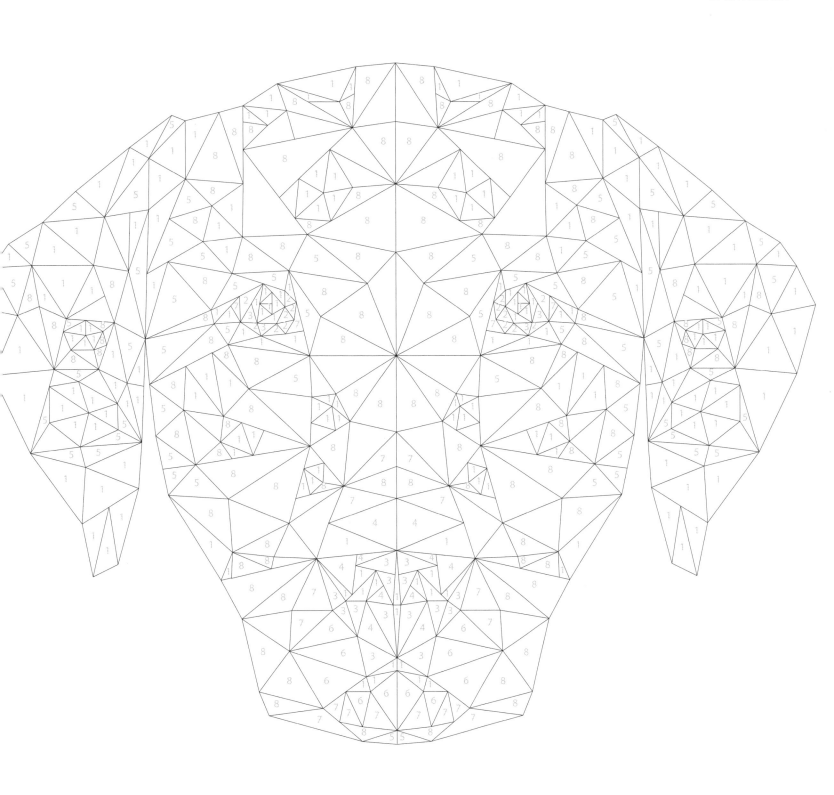

Doberman Pinscher

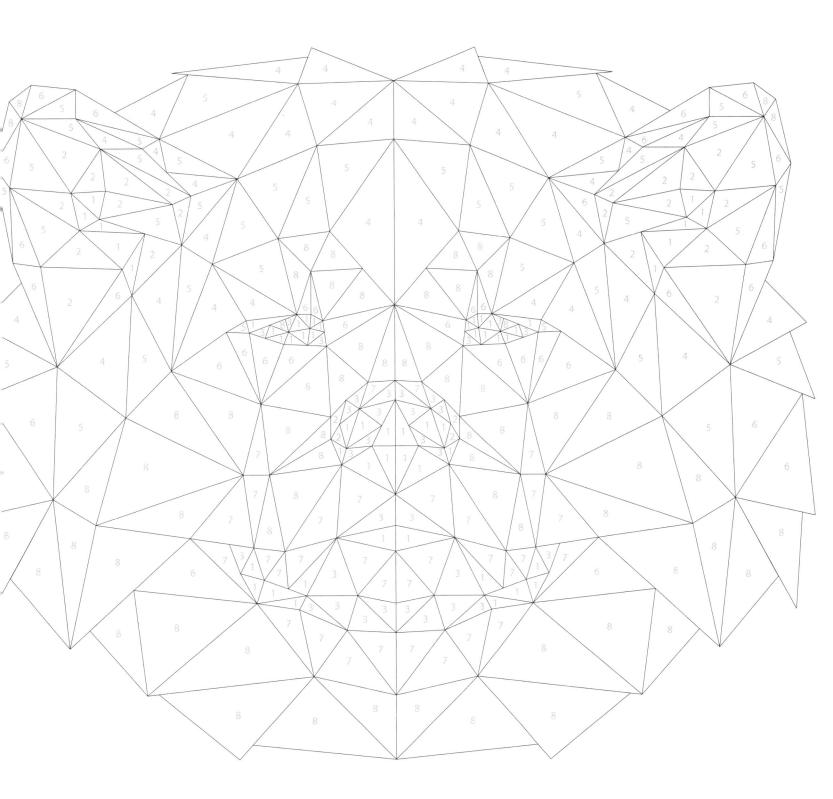

German Wirehaired Pointer

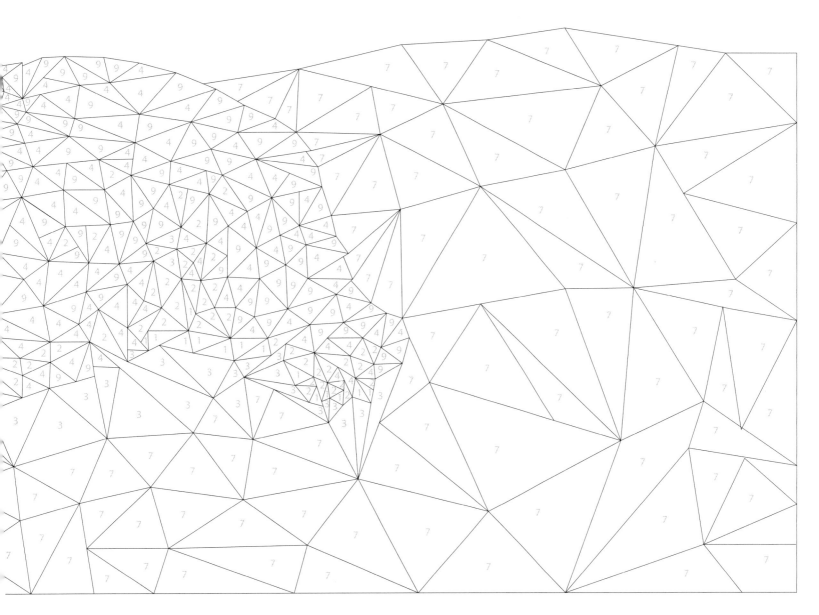

Boxer

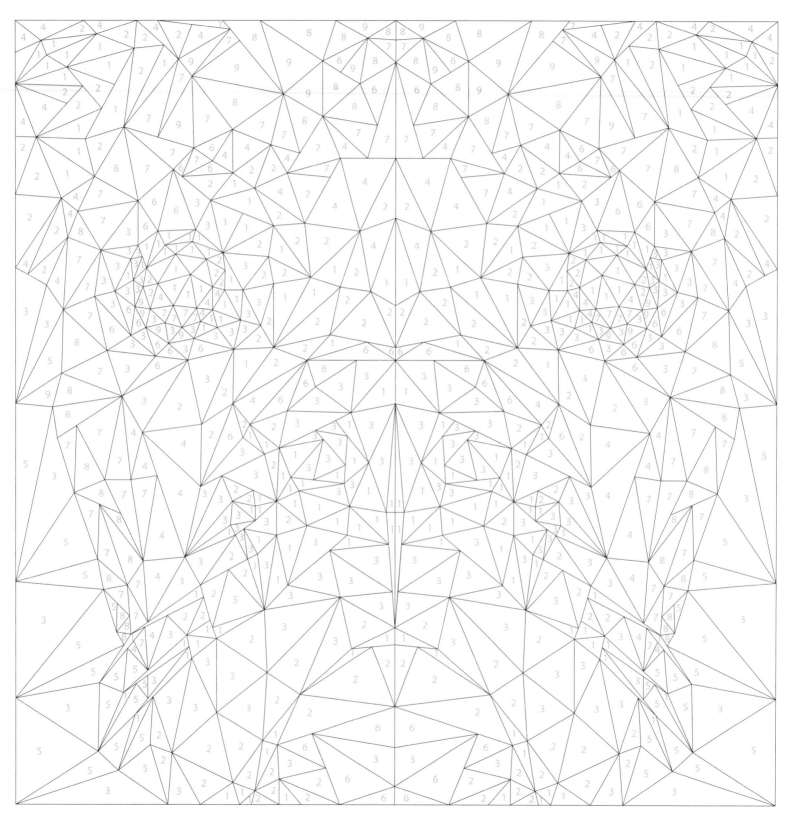

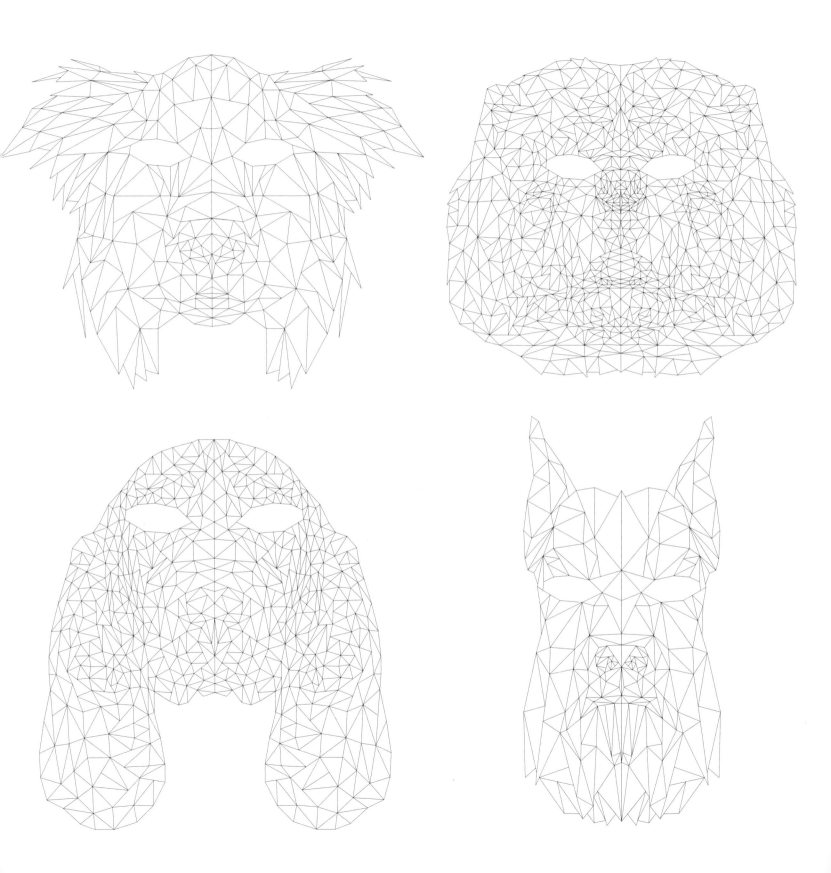

HOW TO MAKE YOUR MASK

Once you have finished colouring your dogs you may want to use them rather than keep them hidden away in the book. You could frame your finished images and create a whole pack of dogs for your wall, adding colour to a dreary corner.

For a fun way to show off your works of art, this section explains how to turn your dogs into masks. With eight templates to choose from, including a Chihuahua, St. Bernard and Basset Hound, there's something for everyone. You could do this as a group activity, maybe in your art class, or at work as part of a team-building session.

CREATE YOUR MASK IN THREE EASY STEPS

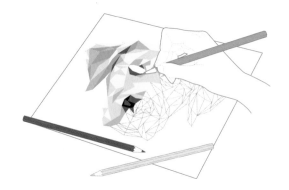  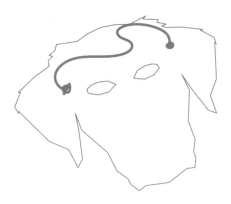

1) Colour in your chosen dog face using the natural or vivid palette.

2) Carefully tear your finished page out of the book – we've added perforated pages to make this easier. Use scissors or a craft knife to cut around the image and then cut out the two eye shapes. At this stage you may want to reinforce the paper with cardboard for extra stability, but this is not essential.

3) Use a piece of elastic that's suitable for tying at the back of your head to keep the mask in place. Make two small holes on either side of the mask; this is where you will attach the elastic. You can use hole reinforcement stickers (available at craft and stationery shops) so that the elastic doesn't tear your mask. Tie the elastic firmly in place on both sides of the mask. Now you are ready to show off your wild side.

Chihuahua

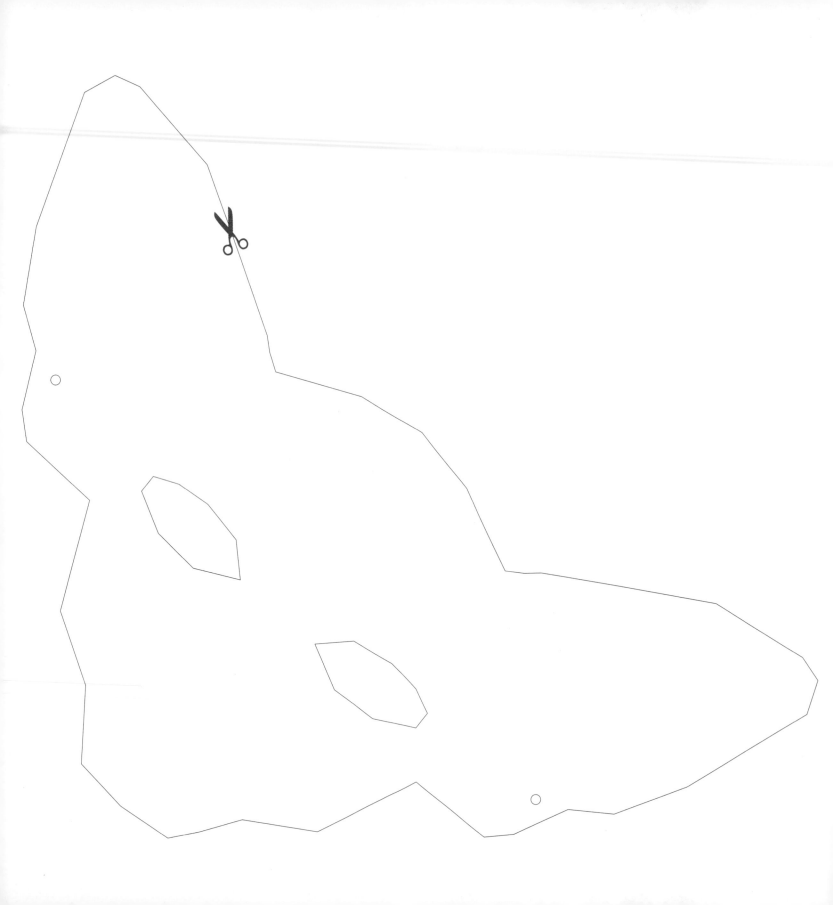

Labrador

VIVID

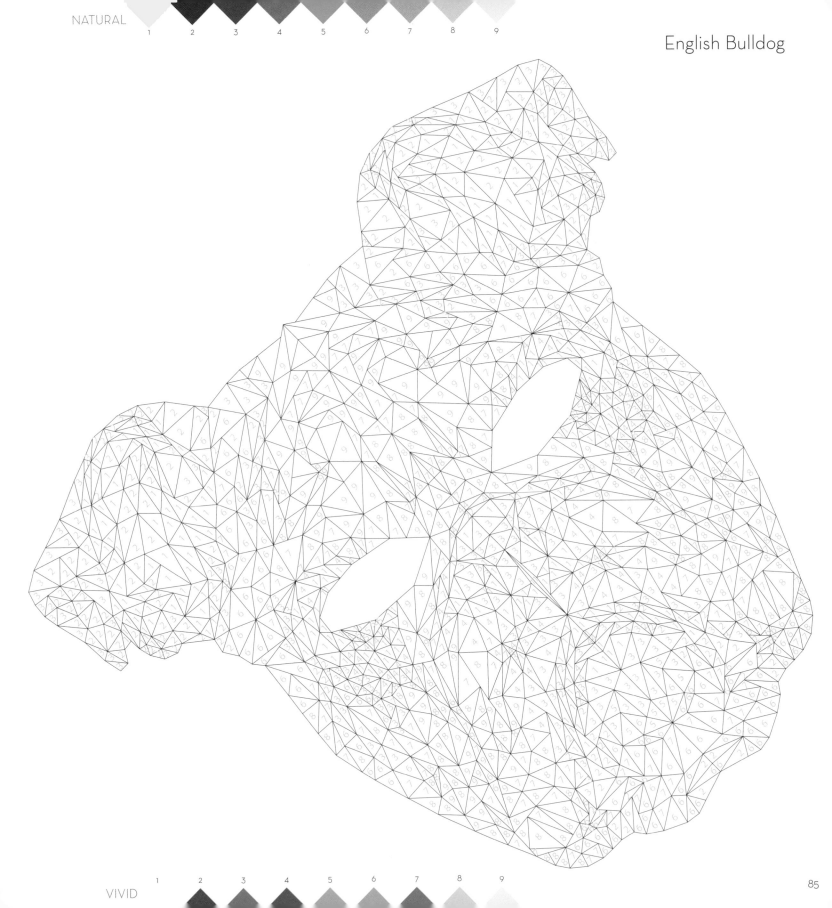

St. Bernard

1 2 3 4 5 6 7 8 9

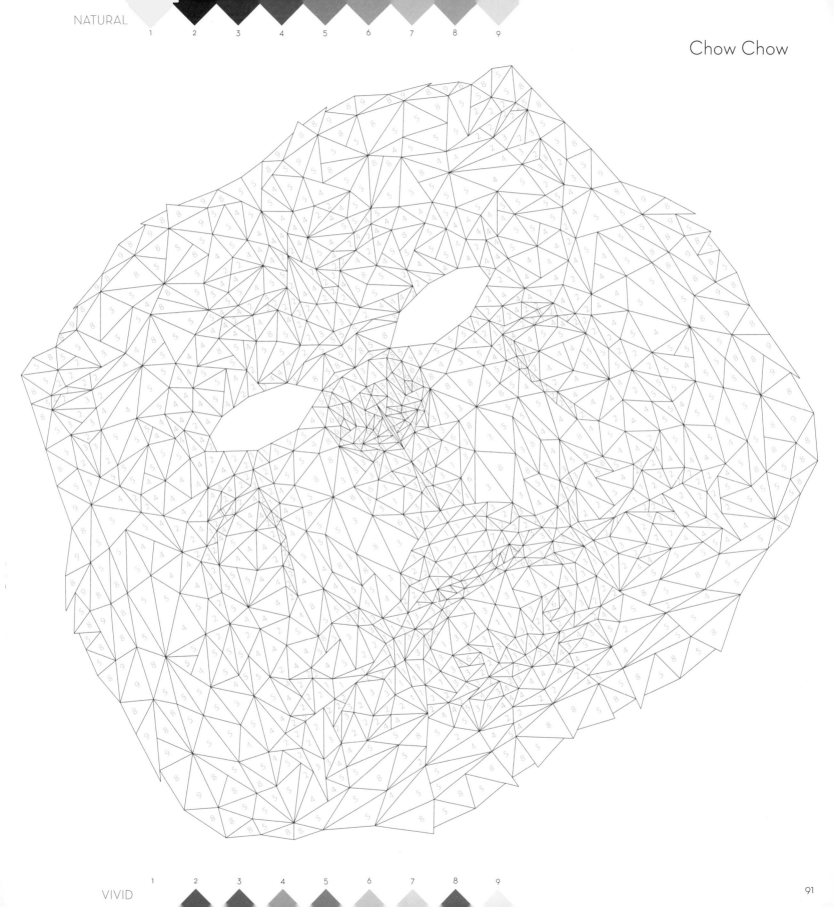

1 2 3 4 5 6 7 8 9

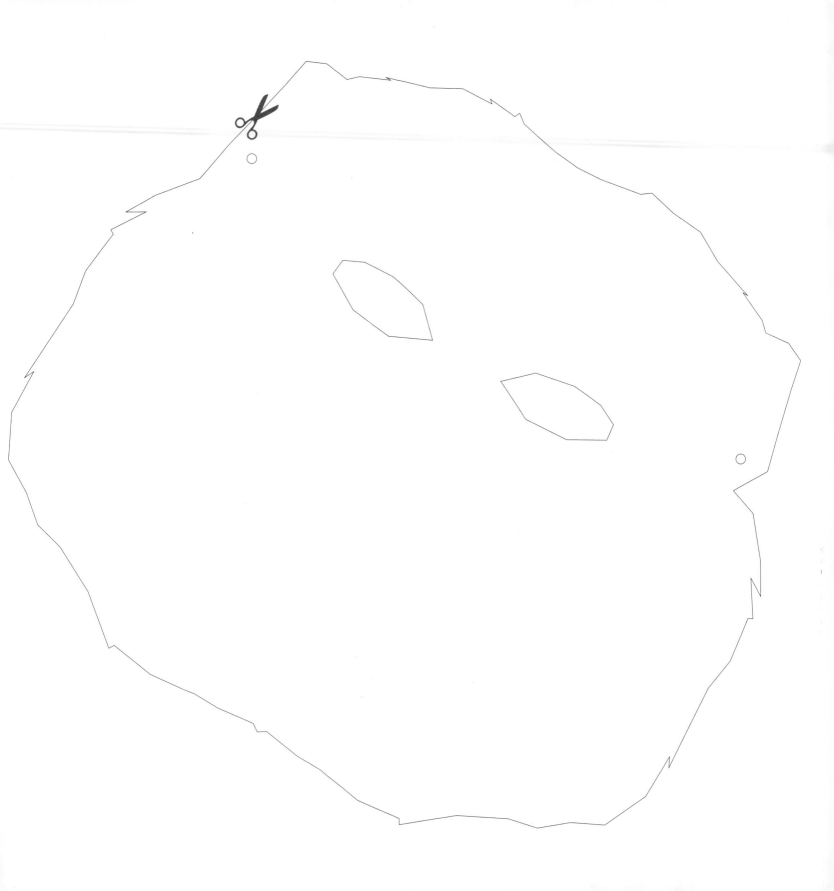

Miniature Schnauzer

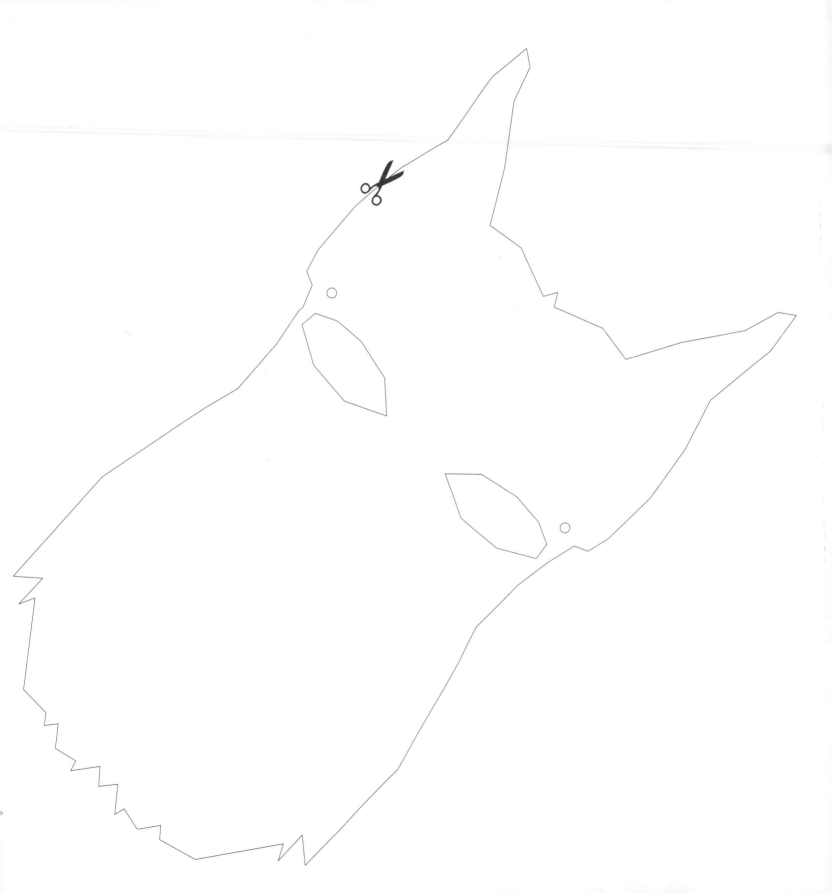

Basset Hound